A TRIVIA MATH ALGEBRA

Katherine Pedersen
Sandra Gadel
Norma Jackson
Paul R. Kosuth
Mary Ann Mings
Kimberly J. Naas
Susan Nogan
Alison Simpson Owens
Petra Wegerich
Joseph Willett

Creative Publications

NOTES TO THE TEACHER

Trivia Math: Algebra was designed as a problem-solving supplement for first-year high school algebra. Algebraic concepts appear in the following sequence: variable expressions, real number properties, solutions of equations in one variable, polynomials, factoring, algebraic fractions, linear systems, functions, inequalities, rational/irrational numbers, and quadratics. (Algebraic fractions come approximately at the midpoint of the book.) The sequence of topics reflects a desire to preserve their relative order as presented in most beginning algebra texts. Once introduced, a topic is reused throughout the remainder of the book.

Monday, Wednesday, and Friday problems deal with subjects usually taught in an algebra course, with the Monday problems being more straightforward than the Wednesday or Friday ones. Thursday problems are nonroutine algebra problems that call for extra thought, ability, insight, or time. Tuesday problems include topics from the history of arithmetic and algebra, puzzles, and questions of a "trivial" nature.

You can use the daily problems in several ways: a problem a day for a small group for the Thursday problems; team competition, with each team trying to answer a problem for each day of the week, out of, say, three weeks' worth of problems; daily warm-ups; or extra credit. You could also use a quiz show format, with teams choosing and answering questions based upon a category (day of the week).

Trivia Math: Algebra can also be viewed as a comprehensive review of algebra for students who have completed Algebra I. In this context, you might integrate the quiz show format into a subsequent math course, as a means of reviewing processes and updating skills.

The Extra Challenge problems are a collection of 36 problem-solving situations that complement and extend the algebraic curriculum. The first challenge problems are straightforward, and their level of difficulty increases very slowly. Many of the problems emphasize using algebra to communicate and to describe patterns. Each Extra Challenge problem requires several days' time, during which the students attempt to solve the problem, and then have a general discussion of attempted solutions. Some of the problems, i.e. figurate number patterns, prime and composite number properties, and cryptarithms, could be developed into independent study or math-science fair projects.

Trivia Math: Algebra is an attempt to put together a collection of nonroutine, problem-solving, enjoyable situations that have a direct relationship to first-year algebra. The task has been enjoyable, and we hope that you and your students will enjoy the result.

The Authors

Edited by Sandra Ward
Cover design by JoAnne Hammer

© 1987 Creative Publications
P.O. Box 10328
Palo Alto, California 94303
Printed in U.S.A.

ISBN 0-88488-643-3

1 2 3 4 5 6 7 8 9 10. 8 9 8 7

MONDAY

Evaluate: $\dfrac{10! - 9!}{8!}$

TUESDAY

Change one sign in the following expression to double the value:

$$61 - 12 - 5 - 13 - 6 - 8 - 7$$

WEDNESDAY

If the greatest common factor of *a* and *b* is 3, what values are possible for the greatest common factor of a^2 and *b*?

THURSDAY

Arrange the digits 1 through 8 in the figure so that no two consecutive integers touch at a side or a corner.

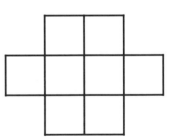

FRIDAY

Place parentheses to make the equation true:

$$36 \div 4 + 5 - 1 + 2 \times 3 + 12 \div 3 + 1 = 6$$

A Small Problem

Using the digits 2, 3, 5, 6 and 8, find the smallest possible product.

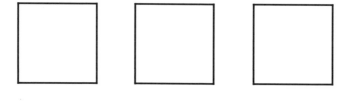

Can you find a pattern so that, given any five distinct digits and using each digit only once, you could write down the smallest possible product of a 2-digit by a 3-digit number?

MONDAY

Arrange in order from least to greatest:

$$\frac{6}{25}, \quad \frac{1}{5}, \quad \frac{11}{50}, \quad \frac{8}{33}$$

3

TUESDAY

The mathematician AL-KHOWARIZMI lent his name to the derivation of what mathematics term?

3

WEDNESDAY

A certain number is doubled, then squared, then divided by the multiplicative identity; the result is zero. What was the original number?

3

THURSDAY

Divide 1000 into two parts so that one part is a multiple of 19 and the other is a multiple of 47.

3

FRIDAY

What number must be added to the numerator and the denominator of $\frac{2}{11}$ to produce a fraction equivalent to $\frac{1}{2}$?

3

Summer Vacation

During the summer vacation, Anita, Brent, Carlos, and Donna worked together picking peaches. At the end of the season, they compared the amount of peaches that they each had picked. They made note of the following facts:

1. Brent picked more than Anita and Carlos picked together.

2. The total of what Anita and Brent picked just equaled the amount Carlos and Donna picked together.

3. The total picked by Donna and Carlos was more than the total picked by Brent and Carlos.

Arrange the names of the people in the order of the amount of peaches that each picked, starting with the person who picked the most.

TRIVIA MATH: ALGEBRA © 1987 Creative Publications

MONDAY

What is the smallest rational number which, when divided either by $\frac{6}{35}$ or by $\frac{10}{21}$, yields an integer quotient?

5

TUESDAY

The set $\{1, 2, 3, \ldots, 15\}$ is partitioned into five subsets, each of which contains exactly three numbers. If the sum of the elements in each subset is to be the same, why cannot $\{6, 8, 9\}$ be one of these subsets?

5

WEDNESDAY

What is the greatest common factor of the following?

$$2(a+b) - 14(a+b)$$

5

THURSDAY

If n is an odd number, then 8 is a factor of

A. n^2

B. $n^2 - 1$

C. $n^2 + 1$

5

FRIDAY

Find a 2-digit number, the sum of whose digits is equal to the square of its cube root.

5

Magic Star!

Place the integers 1, 2, 3, 4, 5, 6, 8, 9, 10, and 12 (7 and 11 are not included) at the intersection of the line segments so that the sum on any line equals the sum on any other line.

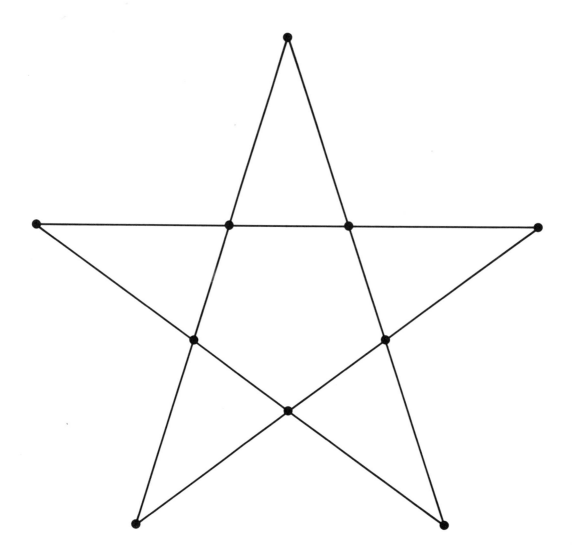

TRIVIA MATH: ALGEBRA © 1987 Creative Publications

MONDAY

Write an expression for the sum of four consecutive odd integers where $2n + 1$ represents the smallest odd integer.

7

TUESDAY

This triangular array of numbers is credited

to _____ .

```
          1
        1   1
      1   2   1
    1   3   3   1
  1   4   6   4   1
 .   .   .   .   .   .
```
7

WEDNESDAY

Which is greater, x or $-x$?

7

THURSDAY

The sum of the first 50 positive odd integers subtracted from the sum of the first 50 positive even integers is _____ .

7

FRIDAY

If a and b are real numbers, what is the name given to the fact that

$$a + b = b + a?$$

7

Square Puzzle

Arrange the squares below into a larger square so that the algebraic expressions on adjacent sides equal the same value upon substitution of $a = 1$, $b = 3$, $c = -4$, $x = \frac{1}{2}$, $y = 10$, $z = -2$.

① czx $b+c$ · · · $\frac{1}{2}by$ x	② $cz-bxy$ b^2 · · · $xz-c$ bc	③ $-y$ $a+b+c$ · · · $b-a$	④ $c+b$ $y-z+bc$
⑤ c^2+bz $-\frac{by}{z}$ · · · $-a$ $c-b$	⑥ xy b^2-z $cx+a$	⑦ $x(y-z)$ $x\cdot c^2$	⑧ $\frac{z}{c}$ $\frac{y^2-a}{b^2}$ · · · $b(a-z)$ $bc-z$
⑨ $y-b$ $-c$	⑩ $2b$ · · · $\frac{yz+c}{cz}$ $|c|$	⑪ $2ax$ $2c+z+y$	⑫ cz $\frac{y+z}{2c}$ $-(a+c+z)$
⑬ $-|c+a|$ · · · a^2 b^2-c-b	⑭ $-|z|$ $xy+z$ $b+|c|$	⑮ $z-y$ $8x^2$ · · · z^2	⑯ $y+5z$ b^2-y cx

TRIVIA MATH: ALGEBRA © 1987 Creative Publications

MONDAY

Which of the following is not true?

A. $8 + (-5) = 3$

C. $-[-8 - (-5)] = 3$

B. $-[-8 + (-5)] = -3$

D. $-8 + (-5) = -13$

9

TUESDAY

Integers having exactly two positive factors are known

as _____.

9

WEDNESDAY

What integers satisfy $x < 4$ and $x \geq 2$?

9

THURSDAY

Use three 9s and one subtraction sign to write an expression equal to 1.

9

FRIDAY

Graph integral solutions to $3x < -1$.

9

Digit-all Problems

Each digit from 1 through 9 appears once and only once in each of these equations:

$$1738 \times 4 = 6952$$
$$1963 \times 4 = 7852$$
$$198 \times 27 = 5346$$
$$138 \times 42 = 5796$$
$$483 \times 12 = 5796$$
$$297 \times \underline{\hphantom{00}} = \underline{\hphantom{0000}}$$
$$186 \times \underline{\hphantom{00}} = \underline{\hphantom{0000}}$$
$$157 \times \underline{\hphantom{00}} = \underline{\hphantom{0000}}$$

Use a calculator to complete this table.

MONDAY

Given that M is the average of two consecutive even integers, write an expression for the smaller even integer.

11

TUESDAY

Under what conditions does the greatest common factor of a and b equal a?

11

WEDNESDAY

What is the coefficient of $x \cdot y$ in the expanded form of

$$(x+y) \ (x+2y) \ (x+3)?$$

11

THURSDAY

If N denotes the square of an integer, what is the next number that is the square of an integer?

11

FRIDAY

$[x]$ is called the *roof* function because $[x]$ is defined as the smallest integer greater than or equal to x. What is $[3\frac{1}{2}]$?

11

A Desert Trek

Assume that one person can carry a 4-day supply of food and water for a trip across a desert that takes 6 days to cross. One person cannot make the trip alone because the food and water would be gone after 4 days. How many persons would have to start out in order for one person to get across and the others to return to the starting point?

TRIVIA MATH: ALGEBRA © 1987 Creative Publications

MONDAY

For what number is {1, 2, 4, 8, 16} the entire set of factors?

13

TUESDAY

If n is an odd number, how would you represent the odd number immediately before it?

13

WEDNESDAY

The square root of one fourth of a number is 8. What is the number?

13

THURSDAY

Find the sum of the positive integers that are both less than 100 and divisible by 6.

13

FRIDAY

What values for a, b, c make $\frac{a+b}{c+b} = \frac{a}{c}$ true?

13

Choose 4!

From the whole numbers 2, 3, 4, 5, 6, . . ., 15, choose four distinct numbers a, b, c, and d such that the following is true.

$$a^2 = b \cdot d$$

and

$$a \cdot d = b^2 c$$

How many different answers exist?

MONDAY

Find the smallest pair of consecutive odd integers whose average is greater than −3.

15

TUESDAY

An integer has a factor of 2 if its units digit has a factor of

_____.

15

WEDNESDAY

Simplify: $(-2a^3b^2)^4 - (-3a^6b^4)^2$

15

THURSDAY

$(x+y)^5 =$

____x^5 + ____x^4y + ____x^3y^2 + ____x^2y^3 + ____xy^4 + ____y^5.

15

FRIDAY

Given two numbers, if you subtract half the smaller number from each number, the result with the larger number is three times as great as the result with the smaller number. How many times as large as the smaller number is the larger number?

15

"I'm not making a mess.
I'm doing a math problem."

Start with a piece of paper. Cut it into 5 pieces. Take any one of the pieces and cut it into 5 pieces. Then, take any one of those pieces and cut it into 5 pieces, and so on. Complete the table below and derive a general rule for the number of pieces you have after the nth time you repeat the cutting process.

Number of times	Number of pieces of paper
0	1
1	

TRIVIA MATH: ALGEBRA © 1987 Creative Publications

MONDAY

A 75-watt bulb is on for 62 hours before it burns out. What is the life of the bulb in kilowatt-hours?

17

TUESDAY

Who is known as the "Prince of Mathematicians?" He discovered the formula

$$\sum_{i=1}^{n} i = \frac{n(n + 1)}{2}.$$

17

WEDNESDAY

Describe the points of intersection of the lines whose equations are the following:

$$4x + 5y = 8$$
$$8x + 10y = 16$$

17

THURSDAY

Automorphic numbers are all integers whose square ends in the given integers such as, $5^2 = 25$ or $6^2 = 36$. Find another automorphic number.

17

FRIDAY

Multiply a nonzero real number by its reciprocal. The result is what?

17

Cryptarithm

A *cryptarithm* is defined as a mathematical problem in which the digits are replaced by letters or words that form sensible words or phrases.

Can you solve these cryptarithms? In each problem, every occurrence of a letter represents the same digit. No number begins with a zero. Letter-number relationships do not carry from one cryptarithm to the next.

```
    FORTY                    TWO
      TEN                  THREE
  +   TEN                + SEVEN
  -------                --------
    SIXTY                  TWELVE
```

MONDAY

On a stereo purchase you are offered a 20% discount and a 10% discount to be taken in either order. Which do you ask for first in order to reach a lower price?

19

TUESDAY

What is the least positive integer by which 180 should be multiplied, to give a product that is (a) a perfect square; (b) a perfect cube?

19

WEDNESDAY

Find a value for the sum of the first n terms of the following series:

$$+1 - 1 + 1 - 1 + 1 - 1 + 1 \ldots$$

19

THURSDAY

The arithmetic mean of five numbers is 2. If the smallest of the five numbers is deleted from the set, the average of the remaining numbers is 4. What is the smallest number in the original set?

19

FRIDAY

In which quadrant(s) are points that satisfy $x \cdot y < 0$?

19

Fill the Boxes!

You are to place one of the digits 0 through 9 in each of the boxes below. You may use a digit more than once; you need not use every digit.

Follow this rule:

The digit you place in the first box (under the 0) is to indicate the total number of zeros in all the boxes; the digit you place in the second box (under the 1) indicates the total number of 1s in all the boxes; and so on, to the last box (under the 9), so that the digit placed there indicates the total number of 9s in all the boxes.

Can you fill in the boxes? It is interesting to note that there is only one correct answer!

0	1	2	3	4	5	6	7	8	9

TRIVIA MATH: ALGEBRA © 1987 Creative Publications

Monday

Write 5445 as a product of primes.

21

Tuesday

If you arrange the numbers 1, 2, . . ., 36 to form a 6 × 6 magic square, what is the sum of each row?

21

Wednesday

What law is illustrated by 6(8+10) = 6•8 + 6•10?

21

Thursday

Given the sequence 1, 4, 9, 16, 25, 36, 49, . . ., you may answer 64 as the next term. What is another rule for this sequence that would not produce 64?

21

Friday

Find all possible values for the greatest common factor of *p* and *q* if *p* and *q* are distinct primes.

21

Diagonal Pattern

What is a formula for the number of diagonals in an n-sided convex polygon, where $n \geq 3$? Complete the table below to help you arrive at an answer.

Number of sides	Figure showing some diagonals	Total number of diagonals
3		0
4		2
5		
6		
7		
8		
.		
.		
.		
n		

TRIVIA MATH: ALGEBRA © 1987 Creative Publications

MONDAY

In an arithmetic sequence, $a_1 = 4$, $a_9 = 972$. What is a_2?

23

TUESDAY

An integer has a factor of 3 if the sum of its digits has a factor of _____ .

23

WEDNESDAY

Simplify:

$$\frac{1}{1 - \dfrac{1}{1+x}} - \frac{1}{\dfrac{1}{1-x} - 1}$$

23

THURSDAY

Is the following statement true or false?

If the least common multiple of a and b equals the least common multiple of a and c, then $b = c$.

23

FRIDAY

Which of the following points is *not* on the line $2x + y = 7$?

$(0, 5)$, $(\frac{7}{2}, 0)$, $(15, -23)$, $(-11, 29)$

23

Equivalent Fractions

$$\frac{3}{6} = \frac{7}{14} = \frac{29}{58}$$

Did you notice that each of these fractions has the same value; and that each of the digits 1 to 9 is used only once?

- Can you find three other fractions, all having the same value, that use each of the digits 1 to 9 only once?

- Is there a third set of fractions that satisfies these conditions?

TRIVIA MATH: ALGEBRA © 1987 Creative Publications

MONDAY

If $8^x = 32$, then $x =$ _____ .

25

TUESDAY

What is the slope of the y-axis?

25

WEDNESDAY

Find the point where $x - 2y = 7$ crosses the x-axis.

25

THURSDAY

The following four statements, and only these, are found on a card:
   On this card exactly one statement is false.
   On this card exactly two statements are false.
   On this card exactly three statements are false.
   On this card exactly four statements are false.
If each statement on the card is either true or false, the number of false statements is exactly _____ .

25

FRIDAY

What is the equation of the line that has a y-intercept of 4 and is parallel to $y = x - 6$?

25

Do All Paths Lead to 1?

Pick any natural number. Is it even or odd?

If it is even, then divide it by 2.

If it is odd, then multiply it by 3 and add 1.

Take the result. Is it even or odd?

If it is even, then divide it by 2.

If it is odd, then multiply it by 3 and add 1.

Take the result. Continue as above.

It has been conjectured that this process ultimately gets to 1 regardless of the number with which you start.

• Take several numbers and try it. Do you always get to 1?

• Can you think of general patterns for numbers that will always get to 1? For example, what about any number of the form 2^n? What about any number of the form 4^n? Are there other patterns?

Monday

Write an equation to express the relationship: Two numbers which differ by 5 have a sum of 19.

27

Tuesday

Before the symbol ∞ was chosen to represent infinity as we know it, the Greeks used the symbol to represent what number?

27

Wednesday

For what values of c does the following have real roots?

$$x^2 + 4x + c = 0$$

27

Thursday

How many zeros are at the end of 20!?

27

Friday

What is the midpoint between the points $(-1, 2)$ and $(3, 4)$?

27

One Way, And Then Back

Pairs of two-digit numbers can have the same product when both numbers are reversed.

$$12 \times 42 = 21 \times 24$$
$$12 \times 63 = 21 \times 36$$
$$12 \times 84 = 21 \times 48$$
$$13 \times 62 = \underline{\hspace{2cm}}$$
$$23 \times \underline{\hspace{1cm}} = \underline{\hspace{2cm}}$$
$$24 \times \underline{\hspace{1cm}} = \underline{\hspace{2cm}}$$
$$26 \times \underline{\hspace{1cm}} = \underline{\hspace{2cm}}$$
$$36 \times \underline{\hspace{1cm}} = \underline{\hspace{2cm}}$$
$$46 \times \underline{\hspace{1cm}} = \underline{\hspace{2cm}}$$

Complete the equations above so the numbers on the right hand side are the reverse of the numbers on the left hand side.

Can you find other pairs?

TRIVIA MATH: ALGEBRA © 1987 Creative Publications

MONDAY

For which nonzero real numbers x is $\dfrac{|x|}{x}$ a positive integer?

29

TUESDAY

Name the famous mathematician who discovered the following theorem: There are infinitely many primes.

29

WEDNESDAY

If $\left[\dfrac{2}{a-b}\right]^2 - \dfrac{4}{a-b} + 1 = 0$, $a \neq b$, then $\dfrac{2}{a-b} = $ _____ .

29

THURSDAY

When you write the numerals 1 through 100, how many times do you write the digit 9?

29

FRIDAY

$$\sum_{n=1}^{24} (-1)^n = \, ?$$

29

Which Column?

The positive integers are arranged in five columns as follows:

	1	2	3	4
8	7	6	5	
	9	10	11	12
16	15	14	13	
	17	18	19	20
.	.	.	.	.
.	.	.	.	.

In which column will the number 999 appear?

 TRIVIA MATH: ALGEBRA © 1987 Creative Publications

MONDAY

In what way can 1000 be expressed as the sum of two or more consecutive numbers?

31

TUESDAY

The symmetric property of equality is illustrated by which of the following:
   A. $10 = 4 + 6$
   B. if $a = b$, then $b = a$
   C. if $a = b$ and $b = c$, then $a = c$

31

WEDNESDAY

What is the slope of the line with equation $4x - 5y = 20$?

31

THURSDAY

The golden ratio is defined as the positive number a that satisfies $\frac{a}{1} = \frac{1}{1+a}$. What is the value of a?

31

FRIDAY

Two candles have different heights and thicknesses. The tall one can burn $3\frac{1}{2}$ hours, the short one 5 hours. After burning 2 hours, the candles are equal in height. Two hours ago, what fraction of the taller candle's height was the shorter candle's height?

31

Fraction Sense

Write down some simple positive fractions.

Make a new fraction whose numerator equals the sum of the numerators, and whose denominator equals the sum of the denominators.

Is the new fraction larger than the smallest one written down? Is it smaller than the largest fraction written down? Will it always be?

TRIVIA MATH: ALGEBRA © 1987 Creative Publications

MONDAY

If $x^2 + bx + q = 0$ has integral roots, with q a prime number, then $b = $ _____ .

33

TUESDAY

What is the units digit of 3^{999}?

33

WEDNESDAY

The measures of the angles of a triangle are in the ratio of 1:2:3. What is the measure of the largest angle?

33

THURSDAY

Different numbers can be obtained by rearranging the digits of the 3-digit number, *abc*. Find the sum of all such numbers.

33

FRIDAY

If $x + 4$ is a factor of a polynomial, then _____ is a root of the polynomial.

33

Digit-all Puzzle

It is true that

$$50\tfrac{1}{2} + 49\tfrac{38}{76} = 100.$$

Can you find another arithmetic expression that uses each of the digits 0 to 9 exactly once to equal 100?

There are several correct answers. How many can you find?

TRIVIA MATH: ALGEBRA © 1987 Creative Publications

Monday

Factor: $400x^2 - 1$

35

Tuesday

An integer has a factor of 5 if its units digit is _____.

35

Wednesday

If the graphs of $3y + x + 4 = 0$ and $2y + ax - 3 = 0$ are to meet at right angles, the value of a is _____.

35

Thursday

One thousand unit cubes are fastened together to form a large cube with edge length 10 units. The cube is dropped in a vat of red paint. How many cubes have at least one face painted?

35

Friday

For which real values of m are the following simultaneous equations satisfied for at least one pair of real numbers, (x, y)?

$$y = mx - 2 \text{ and}$$
$$y = (3m-1)x + 4$$

35

Magic Circles!

Place the integers 1, 2, 3, 4, 5, and 6 at the points of intersection of the circles so that the sum of the integers lying on any given circle is equal to the sum of the integers lying on any other one.

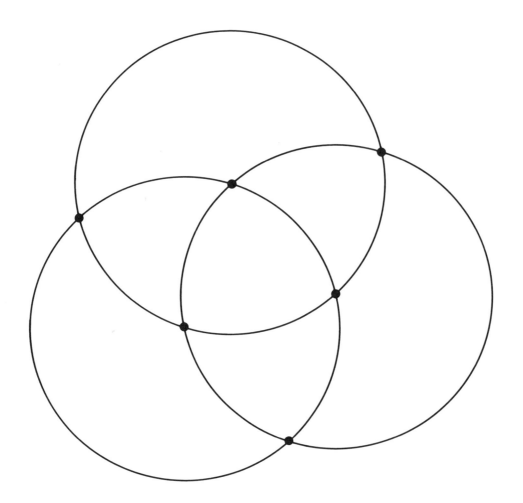

TRIVIA MATH: ALGEBRA © 1987 Creative Publications

MONDAY

Find a value for b such that $4x^2 + bx + 25$ is a perfect square.

37

TUESDAY

Find the smallest integer $n > 1000$ such that n and n^3 end in the same three digits.

37

WEDNESDAY

Fill in the blanks with *directly* or *inversely*.

In $x = \dfrac{Ky}{z}$

x varies _____ as y does.

x varies _____ as z does.

37

THURSDAY

Who was the mathematician who fixed the custom of employing the letters at the beginning of the alphabet as constants and those at the end of the alphabet as variables?

37

FRIDAY

The graph of $3x + 4y = 8$ is closest to which of the following?

A.   B.   C.

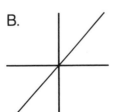   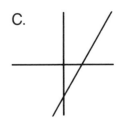

37

Fibonacci Sequence

1, 1, 2, 3, 5, 8, 13, 21, 34, 55, . . .

Except for the first two numbers in the sequence above, each term is the sum of the two terms that precede it in the sequence, as shown below.

$$2 = 1 + 1$$
$$3 = 1 + 2$$
$$5 = 2 + 3$$
$$\cdot$$
$$\cdot$$
$$\cdot$$

$$a_n = a_{n-2} + a_{n-1}, \, n \geq 3$$

Another pattern develops from the terms in the Fibonacci sequence:

$$1^2 + 1^2 = 1 \times 2$$
$$1^2 + 1^2 + 2^2 = 2 \times 3$$
$$1^2 + 1^2 + 2^2 + 3^2 = 3 \times 5$$
$$\cdot$$
$$\cdot$$
$$\cdot$$

Generalize this pattern. Check to see if your generalization works for more terms in the Fibonacci sequence.

MONDAY

Write a proportion that indicates that 50% of a number is 17.

39

TUESDAY

A *twin prime* is a set of two consecutive odd primes, such as (11, 13). Find at least two more sets of twin primes.

39

WEDNESDAY

Find two integers whose sum is 12 and whose product is a maximum.

39

THURSDAY

Find a general formula for the least common multiple of p and q if p and q are distinct primes.

39

FRIDAY

$$\frac{1}{a-b} + \frac{2}{b-a} + \frac{3}{a-b} + \frac{4}{b-a} + \frac{5}{a-b} + \frac{6}{b-a} + \frac{7}{a-b} + \frac{8}{b-a} = \frac{?}{a-b}$$

39

Magic Squares

The magic square below is the oldest known example of a magic square.

4	9	2
3	5	7
8	1	6

According to myth, these number relationships were used to decorate the back of a divine tortoise in 2200 B.C. Be that as it may, magic squares have become a source of mathematical problems.

An *n*th order *magic square* is a square array of n^2 distinct integers arranged so that any row, column, or main diagonal adds to the same number, called the *magic constant* of the square.

Thus, the magic square above is a 3rd order magic square using $3^2 = 9$ distinct integers. If you check, each row, say $4 + 9 + 2$, adds to 15; so does each column, and main diagonal.

A 4 × 4 square has been started below. Using the integers 1, 2, 3, . . . , 16, fill in the blanks so that the result is a 4th order magic square. What will be the magic constant?

16		3	
	11		
			1

How many 4th order magic squares that are essentially different, not just interchanges of rows and columns, can you make?

MONDAY

$$63s^{13}a^4 = ? \cdot 7s^6a^9$$

41

TUESDAY

The following theorem is associated with what mathematician?

There are no integers x, y, z such that
$x^n + y^n = z^n$ for $n \geq 3$.

41

WEDNESDAY

Solve the values for x and y that satisfy both equations:

$$2(x-y) = 3 + x$$
$$x = 3y + 4$$

41

THURSDAY

Complete the following
multiplicative magic square.

45	1	75
25	15	

41

FRIDAY

What is the y-intercept of the line with equation

$$2x + 3y = 4?$$

41

Find the Sum

Complete as much of the following table as you need to in order to find a pattern that will give you the sum ($n \geq 1$):

$$\frac{1}{1 \cdot 3} + \frac{1}{3 \cdot 5} + \cdots + \frac{1}{(2n-1)(2n+1)} + \cdots + \frac{1}{255 \cdot 257}$$

n	Sum	Value of Sum
1	$\frac{1}{1 \cdot 3}$	$\frac{1}{3}$
2	$\frac{1}{1 \cdot 3} + \frac{1}{3 \cdot 5}$	
3	$\frac{1}{1 \cdot 3} + \frac{1}{3 \cdot 5} + \frac{1}{5 \cdot 7}$	
4		
5		
.		
.		
.		

MONDAY

20 km/hour is how many km per 15 minutes?

43

TUESDAY

For what integral values of a, b, c, and d does

$$\frac{a}{b} + \frac{c}{d} = \frac{a+c}{b+d}; \quad b \neq 0; \quad d \neq 0?$$

43

WEDNESDAY

Simplify:

$$\frac{x^2 - y^2}{x - y} \cdot \frac{x + y}{x^2 + 2xy + y}$$

43

THURSDAY

If $\frac{a}{b}$ and $\frac{c}{d}$ are rational numbers with $\frac{1}{2} \leq \frac{a}{b} \leq \frac{c}{d} < 1$, arrange the

following in increasing order:

$$\frac{b}{a}, \; \frac{d}{c}, \; \frac{bd}{ac}, \; 1$$

43

FRIDAY

When one ounce of water is added to a mixture of alcohol and water, the new mixture is 20% alcohol. When one ounce of alcohol is added to the new mixture, the result is $33\frac{1}{3}$% alcohol. What was the percentage of alcohol in the original mixture?

43

Harmonic Triangle

The *Harmonic Triangle* is usually associated with the mathematics of Gottfried Wilhelm Leibniz, one of the mathematicians credited with the discovery of the calculus. The *Harmonic Triangle* deals with the addition and subtraction of fractions and contains several interesting patterns.

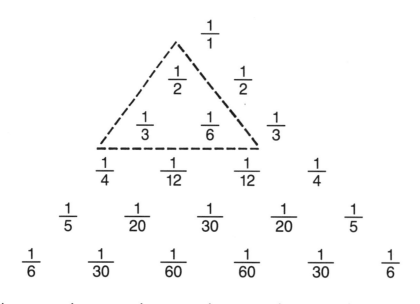

One pattern you may notice is that each row is symmetric: it reads the same left to right as right to left.

- Can you find other patterns? How are the first and last numbers of each row formed?

Look at the three fractions enclosed in the triangle. You may have already noted that $\frac{1}{2} \times \frac{1}{3} = \frac{1}{6}$. Did you also note that $\frac{1}{2} - \frac{1}{3} = \frac{1}{6}$?

Place another triangle around another three fractions, say around $\frac{1}{6}$, $\frac{1}{12}$, and $\frac{1}{12}$. Again, note that $\frac{1}{6} - \frac{1}{12} = \frac{1}{12}$.

In fact, no matter where you place the triangle, the difference of the bottom left-hand fraction from the top fraction is the bottom right-hand fraction.

- Place the triangle in several places and try it.

- Use this "triangle" rule to complete the seventh row of the harmonic triangle. Complete the eighth row.

- Use the "triangle" rule to find the value of the following:
  $\frac{1}{2} + \frac{1}{6} + \frac{1}{12} + \frac{1}{20} + \frac{1}{3} + \cdots$

MONDAY

Simplify: $\dfrac{x^2ym + xym}{xym}$

45

TUESDAY

When the Moors reached Spain in the Middle Ages, they introduced the word ALGEBRA. What did the word algebra originally mean?

45

WEDNESDAY

Write a polynomial of least degree that can have each of 1, 2, 3, 4, 5 as roots.

45

THURSDAY

For what integers a and b, $a \neq b$, does $\dfrac{a}{b} + \dfrac{b}{a} = n$, where n is an integer?

45

FRIDAY

Which of the following polynomials are factorable with real number coefficients?

$$x^2 + 4; \; x^2 - 3; \; x^2 + x + 1$$

45

Perfect Numbers; Amicable Numbers

The Pythagoreans took some of the first steps toward mixing mathematics and mysticism. They studied abstract relationships connecting numbers and ascribed personality traits to certain of the numbers.

It may not be surprising, then, that the ancients called certain numbers *perfect*. A number is called *perfect* if it is the sum of its proper (less than itself) divisors. For example, 1, 2, and 3 are the proper divisors of 6, and 6 = 1 + 2 + 3. Thus 6 is perfect.

• Can you find two more perfect numbers? It may help to know the following statement, which was shown to be true by Euclid:

If $2^n - 1$ is prime, then $(2^n - 1) \cdot 2^{n-1}$ is perfect.

The Pythagoreans also identified another type of number, or, actually, a number pair: two numbers are called *amicable* if each is the sum of the proper divisors of the other. Consider, for example, 220 and 284. The proper divisors of 220 are 1, 2, 4, 5, 10, 11, 20, 22, 44, 55, 110; these sum to 284. The proper divisors of 284 are 1, 2, 4, 71, 142; these sum to 220.

• Can you show that 1184 and 1210 form an amicable pair?

• Very few perfect numbers are known; over 1000 pairs of amicable numbers are known. You may want to use a computer to help you find other amicable pairs.

Monday

Find two numbers such that the sum of their squares is 47 and the difference of their squares is 7.

47

Tuesday

Is the following statement true or false?

In 1975, 2^{216091} was discovered to be the largest prime known to date.

47

Wednesday

What is an equation for the line through the points (5, 3) and (5, −2)?

47

Thursday

What two whole numbers, neither containing any zeros, when multiplied together equal exactly 1,000,000,000?

47

Friday

If 100 km = 60 miles, then 300 miles = _____ km.

47

Factors!

Let $d(n)$ denote the number of factors of the integer n, including 1 and n.
Complete the following table:

n	2	3	4	5	6	7	8	9	10	11	12	13	14
$d(n)$	2	2	3										

n	15	16	17	19	25	27	30	36	41	49	53	64	
$d(n)$													

Conjecture generalizations as follows:

1. If p is prime, $d(p)$ = _____.

2. If p is prime, $d(p^2)$ = _____.

3. If p is prime, $d(p^3)$ = _____.

4. If p is prime, $d(p^n)$ = _____.

5. If $d(n)$ is odd, n is _____.

TRIVIA MATH: ALGEBRA © 1987 Creative Publications

Monday

What is a formula for the nth term of the following sequence?

$+1, \ -1, \ +1, \ -1, \ \ldots$

49

Tuesday

The ampersand (&) was the original symbol for which mathematical process?

49

Wednesday

Does (1, 2) belong to the graph of $3y \leq 2x + 1$?

49

Thursday

How can you split a round clock face so that the sums of the numbers on the two halves are the same?

49

Friday

Factor $x^3 - 7x + 6$ given that $x + 3$ is a factor.

49

Football! Football?

In a certain football game, a team can score only 3 or 7 points at any one time. What is the largest number that could not be a team score in the game?

Continue the table to help you answer the question.

Team Score	Points Used
1	not possible
2	not possible
3	3
4	not possible
5	not possible
6	3 + 3
7	7
8	not possible
9	3 + 3 + 3
10	
11	
12	
.	
.	
.	

- Make a similar table, assuming the team can score only 4 or 7 points at any one time. What is the largest number that could not be a team score using these two numbers?

- What if the team can score only 3 or 8 points at any one time? Make a table, again, to help you decide what is the largest number that could not be a team score.

- What if the team can score only 5 or 7? Only 5 or 8? Only 4 or 9? Only 3 or 6? Only 4 or 8?

MONDAY

What is the slope of the line through points (0, −4) and (3, −10)?

51

TUESDAY

What algebraic rule is represented by the following picture?

	a	b	
b	ab	b^2	b
a	a^2	ab	a
	a	b	

51

WEDNESDAY

Sketch the graph of $\{(x, y) : x < y \text{ and } x > 0\}$.

51

THURSDAY

At precisely what time between one and two o'clock is the minute hand exactly over the hour hand?

51

FRIDAY

If the only roots of a quadratic equation are −2 and 3, what is the equation?

51

TIME is the Problem!

1. Lori goes to lunch not long after 12:00 noon. As she leaves she observes the exact placement of the clock's hands. On her return, she notices that the minute and hour hand have exchanged places. At what time does she return?

2. Craig begins to solve a problem at the time between 4:00 and 5:00 p.m. when the clock's hands are together. He finishes when the minute hand is exactly opposite the hour hand. How many minutes does it take Craig to solve the problem, and at what time does he finish it?

TRIVIA MATH: ALGEBRA © 1987 Creative Publications

MONDAY

Find positive integers x and y such that

$$\frac{1}{x} + \frac{1}{y} = \frac{1}{12}.$$

53

TUESDAY

The word _____ comes from the Greek word for "sand tray" and can be called the earliest mechanical computing device used by man.

53

WEDNESDAY

The square root of the difference of two numbers is 4. The sum of the two numbers is 20. What are the numbers?

53

THURSDAY

Find the units digit in 2^{74}.

53

FRIDAY

What is the maximum number of times the graph of $f(x) = x^4 + x^3 + 1$ can intersect the x-axis?

53

Steps! Steps!

The figures below are constructed of stair-patterned sets of squares. We will let n represent the number of squares on a side. The letter N will represent the number of edges in each pattern. That is, for $n = 1, 2, 3, 4$; $N = 4, 10, 18, 28$.

What are the next three values of N?

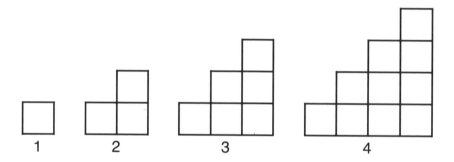

TRIVIA MATH: ALGEBRA © 1987 Creative Publications

MONDAY

Find a quadratic equation with integral coefficients having $\sqrt{7}$ and $-\sqrt{7}$ as roots.

SS

TUESDAY

$[x]$ denotes the greatest integer $\leq x$. What is $[-\frac{1}{2}]$?

SS

WEDNESDAY

Draw the graph of the solution set of real numbers that satisfy

$$a(a-5) > 0.$$

SS

THURSDAY

Which graph represents the time it takes to travel 100 miles as a function of your average speed?

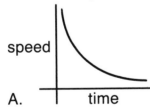 A.

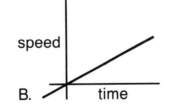 B.

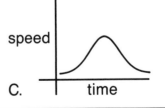 C.

SS

FRIDAY

Rationalize the denominator.

$$\frac{x}{\sqrt{7} - \sqrt{3}}$$

SS

Magic Squares Revisited

Mathematicians really do look for patterns. There is a pattern for finding a magic square of any *odd* order.

To complete a 5th order magic square, follow these instructions:

1. Draw a square and divide it into 5 rows and 5 columns. (See picture below.)

2. Add an extra row to the top of the square; add an extra column to the right of the square.

3. Write 1 in the middle cell of the top row of the original square.

4. Proceed diagonally upward with successive integers.

   - If rule 4 takes you out of the original square, wrap around the square, either top to bottom or right side to left. Note, for example, that "2" is at the bottom of the fourth column since its original placement was out of the square.

   - If rule 4 takes you to an occupied cell, just shift to the cell directly below the one just filled. For example, after writing "5," we want to put a "6" in the cell occupied by 1. So we drop directly below 5 and write the 6. We consider the top right corner to be filled.

   Follow rule 4 until the square is complete.

	18	25	2	9	Filled
17	24	1	8	15	17
23	5	7	14	16	23
4	6	13	20	22	4
10	12	19	21	3	10
11	18	25	2	9	

   - Construct a 7th order magic square, using the instructions above and the integers 1 to 49.

TRIVIA MATH: ALGEBRA © 1987 Creative Publications

MONDAY

Which one of the following is not an irrational number?

A. $\sqrt{3} \cdot \sqrt{4}$ B. $\sqrt{2} \cdot \sqrt{2}$ C. $\sqrt{3} - \sqrt{2}$

57

TUESDAY

The discovery of irrational numbers is usually credited to

_____ .

57

WEDNESDAY

How many times will the graph of $f(x) = x^4 + x^2 + 1$ intersect the x-axis?

57

THURSDAY

Do there exist integers x and y such that

$$x^2 - y^2 = 48?$$

57

FRIDAY

Identify the figure that results from graphing

A. $x^2 - 4y^2 = 16$

B. $x^2 + 4y^2 = 16$

C. $x^2 + 4y = 16$

57

Guess a Pattern!

It is true that:

$$2^1 = 2^2 - 2$$
$$2^1 + 2^2 = 2^3 - 2$$
$$2^1 + 2^2 + 2^3 = 2^4 - 2$$

$$\vdots$$

- Continue with this list until you find a general rule for

$$2^1 + 2^2 + 2^3 + \ldots + 2^n = \underline{\hspace{2cm}} .$$

Does your rule always work? Check it out for several positive integers, n.

- What is a general rule for

$$2^0 + 2^1 + 2^2 + \ldots + 2^n = \underline{\hspace{2cm}} .$$

Does your rule always work? Check it out for several positive integers, n.

MONDAY

A pitcher's ERA (earned run average) is calculated by the formula

$$ERA = 9\left(\frac{a}{b}\right)$$

where a is the total number of earned runs the pitcher has allowed and b is the number of innings the pitcher has pitched. Bob Gibson had an ERA of 1.12 in one of his better seasons. If he pitched 180 innings that year, how many runs did he allow?

59

TUESDAY

$b^2 - 4ac$ is an expression from the quadratic formula. What is $b^2 - 4ac$ called?

59

WEDNESDAY

What is the equation of the line with slope 0 and a y-intercept of 6?

59

THURSDAY

Which is greater? When?

$$\frac{1}{x} \quad \text{or} \quad \frac{1}{x+1}$$

59

FRIDAY

For what values of a do the following have one solution?

$$x^2 + y^2 = 4$$

$$(x-3)^2 + y^2 = a^2$$

59

Triangle Puzzle

Arrange the triangles to form an equilateral triangle so that polynomials on adjacent edges have *at least* one root in common.

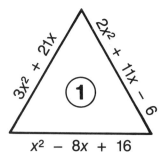

1: $3x^2 + 21x$ / $2x^2 + 11x - 6$ / $x^2 - 8x + 16$

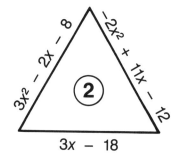

9: $x^2 + 2x + 1$ / $-2x^2 + 9x - 4$ / $-x^2 + 5x - 4$

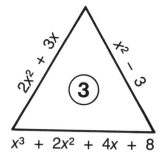

5: $5x - x^2$ / $6x^2 - 13x + 5$ / $x^2 - 6x$

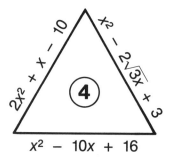

2: $3x^2 - 2x - 8$ / $-2x^2 + 11x - 12$ / $3x - 18$

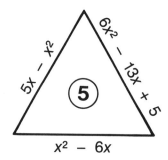

8: $x^2 - 1$ / $3x^2 - 12x - 48$ / $4x^2 - 31x - 8$

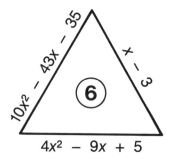

7: $x^2 + x - 6$ / $9x^2 - 6x + 1$ / $4x^2 + 31x + 8$

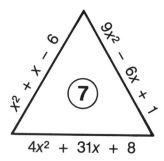

3: $2x^2 + 3x$ / $x^2 - 3$ / $x^3 + 2x^2 + 4x + 8$

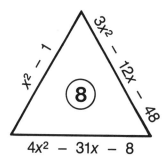

4: $2x^2 + x - 10$ / $x^2 - 2\sqrt{3}x + 3$ / $x^2 - 10x + 16$

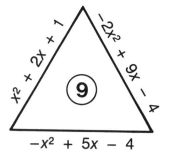

6: $10x^2 - 43x - 35$ / $x - 3$ / $4x^2 - 9x + 5$

MONDAY

Describe the graph of $(x-3)^2 + (y-6)^2 = 4$.

6¹

TUESDAY

Name the first prominent woman mathematician who lectured on algebra of 1st and 2nd degree equations.

6¹

WEDNESDAY

A line perpendicular to the y-axis has slope equal to

_____ .

6¹

THURSDAY

Suppose that p is any prime greater than 3. Determine whether the following statement is true or false: p^2 leaves a remainder of 1 when it is divided by 12. Try various numbers and decide.

6¹

FRIDAY

Factor: $81r^2 - 198rs + 121s^2$

6¹

Triangular and Square Numbers

The ancient Greeks were very interested in geometry and often used geometric representations in their study of arithmetic and algebra. Whole numbers that could be represented by geometric figures were called *figurate numbers*. Two particular types of figurate numbers are the triangular and the square numbers.

Triangular numbers are those which can be represented by a triangular array of dots, *n* on each side.

$n=1$ $n=2$ $n=3$ $n=4$ . . .

If T(*n*) denotes the *n*th triangular number, then we have the following:

n	1	2	3	4	5	6	7	8	. . .
T(*n*)	1	3	6						

- Complete the table above as far as needed to find a general formula for T(*n*).

- Find a formula for T(*n*) that involves the variable *n* and another formula that involves T(*n*−1).

$$T_n = T(n-1) + n.$$

$$T_\partial =$$

MONDAY

The minimum value of $f(x) = (x-2)^2$ occurs when

$x =$ _____ .

63

TUESDAY

In what order are the following digits?

0, 2, 3, 6, 7, 1, 9, 4, 5, 8

63

WEDNESDAY

Solve for b:

$$b^2 - 196 = 0$$

63

THURSDAY

This figure is a geometric representation of what algebraic equation?

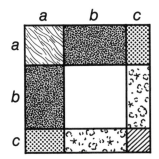

63

FRIDAY

Multiply and simplify:

$$\frac{x^2 + x - 6}{x^2 - 4x - 21} \cdot \frac{x^2 - 8x + 7}{x^2 - x - 2}$$

63

Cubic Generalizations

Examine the following relationships:

$$1^3 = 1^2 - 0^2$$
$$2^3 = 3^2 - 1^2$$
$$3^3 = 6^2 - 3^2$$
$$4^3 = 10^2 - 6^2$$

$$\cdot$$
$$\cdot$$
$$\cdot$$

Can you suggest a generalization of these relationships for a pattern for n^3? Check your generalization with other numbers.

Can you use the table to suggest a pattern for the following?

$$1^3 + 2^3 + 3^3 + \ldots + n^3$$

Check your generalization with several numbers.

TRIVIA MATH: ALGEBRA © 1987 Creative Publications

Monday

Write the equation of a circle with center (6, 6) and tangent to both axes.

65

Tuesday

A. M. Turing's famous "Turing machine" is the ancestor of one of our modern tools. Name this tool.

65

Wednesday

Find the coordinates of the vertex of $y = (x-3)^2$.

65

Thursday

What geometric figure is bounded by the lines
$3x + 4y = 6$, $4x - 3y = 18$, the x-axis and the y-axis?

65

Friday

Find at least one value for a between 100 and 200 for which $ax^2 + x - 6$ can be written as the product of two linear factors, each with integer coefficients.

65

A Colorful Puzzle

You are given 12 wooden cubes, all different in size and in color. The largest cube is 12 cm on a side, the next is 11 cm on a side and so on down to the smallest cube, which is 1 cm on a side. The cubes are colored red, blue, orange, yellow, green, purple, silver, white, violet, tangerine, crimson, and mauve. The following relationships hold among the cubes:

1. The sum of the volumes of the yellow and blue cubes equals the sum of the volumes of the green and mauve cubes.

2. The volume of the purple cube alone equals the sum of the volumes of the red, violet, and silver cubes.

3. The sum of the volumes of the blue, orange, purple, and violet cubes equals the sum of the volumes of the mauve, green, tangerine, silver, white, and yellow cubes.

4. The volume of the green cube alone equals the sum of the volumes of the tangerine, purple, and yellow cubes.

Match the size of each of the 12 cubes with its proper color.

Monday

Show that no pair of integers satisfies the equation

$$3x + 6y = 92.$$

67

Tuesday

Let $a * b$ denote the least common multiple of a and b.
Is $a * b$ commutative? Is $a * b$ associative?

67

Wednesday

How many solutions satisfy both $x^2 + y^2 = 100$ and $x^2 + 2y^2 = 8$?

67

Thursday

Consider the set of equations:

$$\begin{cases} ax + y = a^2 \\ x + ay = 1 \end{cases}$$

For what values of a does this system fail to have solutions, and for what values of a are there infinitely many solutions?

67

Friday

If $g(x) = x^2 - 1$ and $f(x) = x^3$ then $f(g(2)) = $ _____ .

67

Figurate Number Patterns

The table below displays several figurate number patterns. Just as there are triangular numbers and square numbers (Extra Challenge 31), there are also pentagonal numbers, hexagonal numbers, and so on. Pentagonal numbers are those which can be represented by a pentagonal (5-sided) array of dots, n on a side; hexagonal numbers are those which can be represented by a hexagonal (6-sided) array of dots, n on a side.

Number Shape \ N	1	2	3	4	5	6	7	8	9
Triangular	1	3	6	10	15	21	28	36	45
Square	1	4	9	16	25	36	49	64	81
Pentagonal	1	5	12	22	35	51	70	92	117
Hexagonal	1	6	15	28	45	66	91	120	153
Heptagonal	1	7	18	34	55	81	112	148	189
Octagonal	1	8							

• There are several patterns in the rows and columns of this table. Find a few.

• What is the 10th triangular number?

• What is the 10th square number?

There is a relationship between the figurate numbers in one row and the figurate numbers in the row directly above and the triangular numbers.

• For example, the pentagonal numbers can be computed by looking at the square numbers and the triangular numbers. Find this pattern and use it to calculate the 10th pentagonal number.

• Find the pattern between the hexagonal numbers and the pentagonal and triangular numbers. Use this pattern to calculate the 10th hexagonal number.

• What is the 10th heptagonal number?

• Complete the row for the octagonal numbers.

MONDAY

Describe the points of intersection of the lines with equations

$$4x + 5y = 6$$
$$8x + 10y = 12.$$

69

TUESDAY

Our word *calculate* is derived from the Roman word *calculus*. What did calculus originally mean?

69

WEDNESDAY

What will be the power of z in the simplified form of

$$\left[\frac{x^{-1} \cdot y}{z^{-1}} \right]^2 \cdot \left[\frac{x^3}{y^{-3}z^{-1}} \right]^{-1} \cdot \left[\frac{z^2 \cdot x}{y^{-3}} \right]^{-2} ?$$

69

THURSDAY

Determine whether the following statement is true or false. The sum of any two irrational numbers is also an irrational number.

69

FRIDAY

If the side of one square is the diagonal of a second square, what is the ratio of the area of the first square to the area of the second?

69

"I'll use my own dice!"

(1, 1)	(1, 2)	(1, 3)	(1, 4)	(1, 5)	(1, 6)
(2, 1)	(2, 2)	(2, 3)	(2, 4)	(2, 5)	(2, 6)
(3, 1)	(3, 2)	(3, 3)	(3, 4)	(3, 5)	(3, 6)
(4, 1)	(4, 2)	(4, 3)	(4, 4)	(4, 5)	(4, 6)
(5, 1)	(5, 2)	(5, 3)	(5, 4)	(5, 5)	(5, 6)
(6, 1)	(6, 2)	(6, 3)	(6, 4)	(6, 5)	(6, 6)

If two dice are tossed, any one of 36 ordered pairs can result: We can get any number from 1 to 6 on the first die, and any number, 1 to 6, on the second.

The probability that the dots showing on top of the dice add to 2 is 1/36, since we get 2 only by (1, 1). The probability that the dots add to 3 is 2/36, since 3 comes from (1, 2) and (2, 1).

Your problem is to design a pair of dice. The rules are:

1. The dice must be cubic in shape (regular-shaped dice with 6 faces each).

2. Use only 2 dice.

3. Every whole number 1, 2, 3, 4, 5, 6, 7, 8, 9, 10, 11, 12 must be able to occur as a sum when the two dice are tossed.

4. Each of the whole numbers 1, 2, 3, 4, 5, 6, 7, 8, 9, 10, 11, 12 must have the same probability of occurring.

MONDAY

What is the smallest integral value of K such that

$$2x(Kx - 4) - x^2 + 6 = 0$$

71

TUESDAY

1. The sieve of _____ refers to prime numbers.
2. The algebra of classes or sets.
3. The invention of "Napier's rods" led to the later discovery of

_____ .

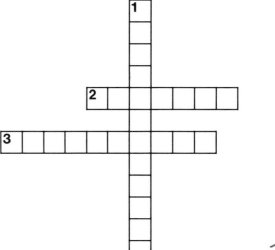

71

WEDNESDAY

Let $f(x) = (x+2)^2 + a$. For what value(s) of a will the graph of $f(x)$ cut the x-axis 0 times? 1 time? 2 times?

71

THURSDAY

Given the ellipse shown at right, can you find the distance d?

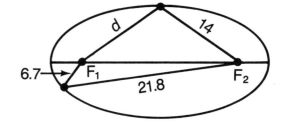

71

FRIDAY

Opposite sides of a regular hexagon are 12 cm apart. The length of each side is _____ .

71

Figurate Numbers: Encore

The table below gives the general formula for several of the figurate numbers.

Number Shape	Formula for the nth Number
Triangular	$T(n) = \dfrac{n^2 + n}{2}$
Square	$S(n) = \dfrac{2n^2 + 0n}{2} = n^2$
Pentagonal	$P(n) = \dfrac{3n^2 - n}{2}$
Hexagonal	$Hx(n) = \dfrac{4n^2 - 2n}{2} = 2n^2 - n$
Heptagonal	$H(n) = \dfrac{5n^2 - 3n}{2}$
Octagonal	
Nonagonal	

In an earlier look at figurate numbers (Extra Challenge 34), we found that pentagonal numbers can be found by looking at square and triangular numbers. Hexagonal numbers were related to pentagonal numbers and triangular numbers, and so on.

We can derive the formulas in this table from that same information:

- Show that $P(n) = S(n) + T(n-1)$.

- Show that $Hx(n) = P(n) + T(n-1)$.

- Show that $H(n) = Hx(n) + T(n-1)$.

- Find the formula for $0(n)$, the nth octagonal number, in a manner similar to the above or generalize from the pattern in the table.

- Find the formula for $N(n)$, the nth nonagonal number.

SOLUTIONS

Page 1

M $\dfrac{9!\,(10-1)}{8!} = 9\cdot 9 = 81$

Tu $61 - 12 + 5 - 13 - 6 - 8 - 7$

W   3 or 9

Th

	3	5	
7	1	8	2
	4	6	

F   There are various answers. One is
$(((((36 \div (4+5)) - (1+2)) \times 3) + 12) \div 3) + 1 = 6.$

Page 2

2	5	8

× | 3 | 6 |

Pattern: If $a_1 < a_2 < a_3 < a_4 < a_5$ are five distinct digits, the smallest possible 2-digit by 3-digit product is $a_1a_3a_5 \times a_2a_4$.

Page 3

M $\frac{1}{5}$, $\frac{11}{50}$, $\frac{6}{25}$, $\frac{8}{33}$

Tu   algorithm

W   0

Th $1000 = 18(19) + 14(47).$
Strategy: Calculate a 19 times table.
Calculate a 47 times table.
Compare the tables.

F $\dfrac{2 + a}{11 + a} = \dfrac{1}{2}$
$4 + 2a = 11 + a$
$a = 7$

Page 4

B=Brent, A=Anita, C=Carlos, D=Donna

1) $B > A + C$
2) $A + B = C + D$
3) $C + D > B + C$
From 2) and 3), we get $A + B > B + C$ or $A > C$.
From 1) we get $B > A$ and $B > C$.
From 3) we get $D > B$.
Thus, $D > B > A > C$ or:
Donna picked the most; then Brent; then Anita; and then Carlos.

Page 5

M $2 \times 5 \times 6$

Tu   The numbers 1, 2, 3, . . ., 15 sum to 120. Each subset must, therefore, contain numbers which add to $120 \div 5 = 24$. The sum of 6, 8, and 9 is 23, not 24.

W $2(a + b)$

Th   B

F   27

Page 6

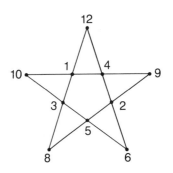

Page 7

M $2n+1 + 2n+3 + 2n+5 + 2n+7 = 8n+16$

T   Pascal

W   You can't tell; the answer depends on whether x is positive or negative.

Th $-1 + 2 - 3 + 4 - 5 + 6 - \ldots - 99 + 100 = 50$

F   The commutative law for addition

Page 8

7	10	13	11
12	1	5	16
6	8	2	14
4	3	15	9

None of the squares is rotated in order to fit.

Page 9

M   B

Tu   prime numbers

W   2, 3

Th $9^{9-9} = 9^0 = 1$

F

```
 ←——•——•——•——•——•——•——•——•——⊕——→
   -8  -7  -6  -5  -4  -3  -2  -1   0
```
All integers ≤ -1.

Page 10

$297 \times 18 = 5346$
$186 \times 39 = 7254$
$157 \times 28 = 4396$

Page 11

M $M-1$

Tu   When b is a multiple of a.

W   9

Th $(\sqrt{N} + 1)^2 = N + 2\sqrt{N} + 1.$

F   4

Page 12

3 people. Persons A, B, & C.

Day 1: Persons A, B, and C eat Person A's food/water.

Day 2: Person A returns, using own remaining food/water. B & C each eat B's food/water.

Day 3: Person B returns, using own remaining food/water. C begins his/her own food/water.

Day 4: C eats own food/water.

Day 5: C eats own food/water.

Day 6: C eats own food, arrives at destination.

Page 13

M	16
Tu	$n-2$
W	256
Th	816
F	$b = 0, c \neq 0$;
	$b \neq 0$, and $a = c, c \neq 0$.

Page 14

Consider 2, 3, 4, 5, 6, 7, 8, 9, 10, 11, 12, 13, 14, 15. $a^2 = b \cdot d$ and $a \cdot d = b^2 c \rightarrow a^3 d = b^3 \cdot c \cdot d$ or $a^3 = b^3 \cdot c$. So, c must be the cube of an integer. The only possible answer from 2 to 15, is $c = 8$. Thus, $a = 2b$. Using $a^2 = b \cdot d$ and $a = 2b$, we get $4b^2 = bd$ or $d = 4b$.

In the range we have, $b = 2 \rightarrow a = 4 \rightarrow d = 8$. If $b = 3$, $a = 6$, and $d = 12$. Possible. If $b = 4$, $a = 8$, $d = 16$. We have no 16 and $c = 8$. So, we must have $b = 3$, $a = 6$, $d = 12$.

Thus, solutions are $a = 6$; $b = 3$; $c = 8$; $d = 12$.

A check of the original equations: $6^2 = 3 \cdot 12$ and $6 \cdot 12 = 9 \cdot 8$ shows the solutions work.

Page 15

M	-3 and -1
Tu	2
W	$7a^{12}b^8$
Th	1, 5, 10, 10, 5, 1
F	twice

Page 16

Number of times	Number of pieces of paper
0	1
1	5
2	9
3	13
4	17
5	21
6	25
⋮	⋮
n	$4n+1$

Page 17

M	75 (watt) $\cdot$ 62 (hours) $= 75 \cdot \frac{1}{1000}$ (kilowatt) $\cdot$ 62 (hours) $= \frac{4650}{1000}$ kilowatt-hours $= 4.65$ kilowatt-hours
T	Carl Friedrich Gauss
W	These are the same line; the points of intersection are all points on the line.
Th	$1^2 = 1$; $(25)^2 = 625$
F	1

Page 18

FORTY	29,786
TEN	850
+ TEN	+ 850
SIXTY	31,486

TWO	106
THREE	19,722
+ SEVEN	+ 82,524
TWELVE	102,352

Page 19

M	You reach the same price either way.
T	(a) $180 = 2^2 \cdot 3^2 \cdot 5$
	Thus, $180 \cdot 5 = 2^2 \cdot 3^2 \cdot 5^2 = (2 \cdot 3 \cdot 5)^2$.
	(b) $180(2 \cdot 3 \cdot 5^2) = 2^3 \cdot 3^3 \cdot 5^3 = (2 \cdot 3 \cdot 5)^3$ Thus, $2 \cdot 3 \cdot 5^2$ times 180 produces a perfect cube.
W	If n is odd, the sum is 1.
	If n is even, the sum is 0.
Th	-6
F	II and IV

TRIVIA MATH: ALGEBRA © 1987 Creative Publications

Page 20

0	1	2	3	4	5	6	7	8	9
6	2	1	0	0	0	1	0	0	0

The strategy for the students should be a process of trial and error. Make sure they understand the rules of the problem by trying a few numbers.

Page 21

M $3^2 \cdot 5 \cdot 11^2$

Tu   36

$$\sum_{i=1}^{36} i = \frac{36(37)}{2} = 666.$$

$666 \div 6 = 111.$

Therefore, each row has to add to 111.

W   Distributive law

Th $N^2 + (N-1)(N-2)(N-3)(N-4)(N-5)(N-6)(N-7)$

F   1

Page 22

Number of Sides	Total Number of Diagonals
3	0
4	2
5	5
6	9
7	14
8	$\frac{8 \cdot 7}{2 \cdot 1} - 8 = 28 - 8 = 20$
9	$\frac{9 \cdot 8}{2 \cdot 1} - 9 = 36 - 9 = 27$
.	
.	
.	
n	$\frac{n(n-1)}{2 \cdot 1} - n = \frac{n^2 - 3n}{2}$

Page 23

M   The sequence is 4, a_2, a_3, . . ., a_8, 972. Thus, if d is the difference between successive terms, then $972 - 4 = 8d$. $d = 121$. So, $a_2 = 4 + 121 = 125$.

Tu   3

W   2

Th   False. For example, LCM(3, 12) = LCM(6, 12) but $3 \neq 6$.

F   (0, 5)

Page 24

$\frac{2}{4} = \frac{3}{6} = \frac{79}{158}$

$\frac{3}{6} = \frac{9}{18} = \frac{27}{54}$

$\frac{2}{6} = \frac{3}{9} = \frac{58}{174}$

Page 25

M $\frac{5}{3}$

Tu   The y-axis has no slope.

W   (7, 0)

Th   Three. Only statement three can be true.

F $-x + y = 4$

Page 26

Regardless of the number chosen, a process such as the following occurs:

7

$7 \times 3 + 1 = 22$

$22 \div 2 = 11$

$11 \times 3 + 1 = 34$

$34 \div 2 = 17$

$17 \times 3 + 1 = 52$

$52 \div 2 = 26$

$26 \div 2 = 13$

$13 \times 3 + 1 = 40$

$40 \div 2 = 20$

$20 \div 2 = 10$

$10 \div 2 = 5$

$5 \times 3 + 1 = 16$

$16 \div 2 = 8$

$8 \div 2 = 4$

$4 \div 2 = 2$

$2 \div 1 = 1$

It is not known whether there are any numbers which do not return ultimately to 1.

Encourage students to write a computer program to carry out the arithmetic.

Page 27

M $x + (x+5) = 19$; $x + (x-5) = 19$; or
       $x + y = 19$ and $x - y = 5$

Tu   10,000

W $\sqrt{b^2 - 4ac} = \sqrt{16 - 4c}$
        $16 - 4c \geq 0$
           $16 \geq 4c$
            $4 \geq c$
    Thus, $c \leq 4$

Th   4

F   (1, 3)

Page 28

$$12 \times 42 = 21 \times 24$$
$$12 \times 63 = 21 \times 36$$
$$12 \times 84 = 21 \times 48$$
$$13 \times 62 = 31 \times 26$$
$$23 \times 96 = 32 \times 69$$
$$24 \times 63 = 42 \times 36$$
$$26 \times 93 = 62 \times 39$$
$$36 \times 84 = 63 \times 48$$
$$46 \times 96 = 64 \times 69$$

Other pairs:
$$14 \times 82 = 41 \times 28$$
$$23 \times 64 = 32 \times 46$$
$$34 \times 86 = 43 \times 68$$
$$13 \times 93 = 31 \times 39$$

Page 29

M   For x positive real numbers

Tu   Euclid

W $\dfrac{2}{a-b} = 1$

Th   20

F   0

Page 30

The pattern develops by 8s. $999 \div 8 = 124$ with remainder 7. Thus 999 would appear in the *second* column.

Page 31

M   One answer: $198 + 199 + 200 + 201 + 202$

Tu   B

W $\frac{4}{5}$

Th $\dfrac{2}{1 + \sqrt{5}} = \dfrac{\sqrt{5} - 1}{2}$

F   Let h_1 be height of shorter candle two hours ago. Let h_2 be height of taller candle two hours ago. Shorter candle burns at rate of $\frac{1}{5}$ every hour. Taller candle burns at rate of $\frac{2}{7}$ every hour. The equation

$$h_1 - \tfrac{2}{5}h_1 = h_2 - \tfrac{4}{7}h_2 \text{ simplifies to } \frac{h_1}{h_2} = \tfrac{5}{7}.$$

Thus, two hours ago, the shorter candle's height was $\frac{5}{7}$ of taller candle's height.

Page 32

Yes.   Yes.   Yes.

Let a/b and c/d be positive fractions, $b \neq 0$, $c \neq 0$, with $a/b < c/d$, $a > 0$, $c > 0$.

We show $a/b < \dfrac{a + c}{b + d} < c/d$.

Since $a/b < c/d$, we have $ad < bc$. Adding ab to both sides, we get $ab + ad < ab + bc$ or $a(b+d) < b(a+c)$. This is the same as

$a/b < \dfrac{a + c}{b + d}$.

If we add cd to both sides of $ad < bc$, we arrive at $ad + dc < bc + dc$ or $d(a+c) < c(b+d)$. This is the same as

$\dfrac{a + c}{b + d} < c/d$.

Given three fractions, $a/b < c/d < e/f$, we propose to show that

$a/b < \dfrac{a + c + e}{b + d + f} < e/f$.

By the case above, with two fractions, we can deduce from $a/b < c/d < e/f$ that

$a/b < \dfrac{a + c}{b + d} < c/d < \dfrac{c + e}{d + f} < e/f$.

Using conclusion from two fractions,

$a/b < \dfrac{c + e}{d + f}$ implies that

$a/b < \dfrac{a + c + e}{b + d + f}$.   (i)

Using the same conclusion on $\dfrac{a + c}{b + d} < e/f$,

we arrive at $\dfrac{a + c + e}{b + d + f} < e/f$.   (ii)

Putting (i) and (ii) together, we get

$a/b < \dfrac{a + c + e}{b + d + f} < e/f$.

This procedure generalizes for 4, 5, 6 or more fractions.

Advanced students could be encouraged to use finite induction to prove if

$\dfrac{a_1}{b_1} < \dfrac{a_2}{b_2} < \ldots < \dfrac{a_n}{b_n}$, then

$\dfrac{a_1}{b_1} < \dfrac{a_1 + a_2 + \ldots + a_n}{b_1 + b_2 + \ldots + b_n} < \dfrac{a_n}{b_n}$ for all natural numbers n, $a_j > 0$, $b_j \neq 0$, $1 \leq j \leq n$.

Page 33

M $\pm(q + 1)$

Tu   The units digit will be 7. There is a pattern:
$3^1 = 3$; $3^2 = 9$; $3^3 = 27$; $3^4 = 51$;
$3^5 = 243$; $3^6 = 729$; ... So the pattern,
3, 9, 7, 1 is repeated every 4 powers of 3
beginning with 1. We find 999 has a
remainder of 3 when divided by 4. So, it will
use the 3rd term of the pattern, 3, 9, 7, 1.

W   90°

Th $222(a+b+c)$

F $x = -4$

Page 34

$0 + 1 + 2 + 3 + 4 + 5 + 6 + 7 + (8 \times 9) = 100$

$78\frac{3}{6} + 21\frac{45}{90} = 100$

$89 + 6\frac{1}{2} + 4\frac{35}{70} = 100$

$90 + 8\frac{3}{6} + 1\frac{27}{54} = 100$

$97\frac{30}{45} + 2\frac{6}{18} = 100$

$97\frac{43}{86} + 2\frac{5}{10} = 100$

$1 + 2\frac{35}{70} + 96\frac{4}{8} = 100$

Page 35

M $(20x - 1)(20x + 1)$

Tu   either 0 or 5

W -6

Th   488

F $m \neq \frac{1}{2}$

Page 36

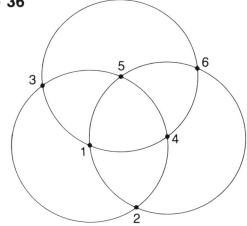

Page 37

M   20

Tu $n = 1001$

W   directly; inversely

Th   René Descartes

F   A

Page 38

Generalization: The sum of the squares of
the first n terms of the Fibonacci sequence
is the product of the nth and $(n + 1)$th
term. It always works.

Page 39

M $\frac{50}{100} = \frac{17}{x}$; or $\frac{17}{50} = \frac{x}{100}$; or $\frac{100}{50} = \frac{x}{17}$;
or $\frac{50}{17} = \frac{100}{x}$

Tu   Various answers of the form $(p, p+2)$ with p
and $p+2$ prime. Some are (3, 5), (11, 13),
(29, 31), (41, 43), (59, 61), (71, 73).

W   6 and 6

Th $p \cdot q$

F -4

Page 40

16	2	3	13
5	11	10	8
9	7	6	12
4	14	15	1

Page 41

M $9s^7a^{-5}$ or $\dfrac{9s^7}{a^5}$

Tu   Pierre Fermat

W $(1, -1)$

Th   The magic constant is $(45)(1)(75) = 3375$.

45	1	75
25	15	9
3	225	5

F $(0, \frac{4}{3})$

Page 42

n	Sum	Value of Sum
1	$\frac{1}{1\cdot3}$	$\frac{1}{3}$
2	$\frac{1}{1\cdot3}+\frac{1}{3\cdot5}$	$\frac{6}{15}=\frac{2}{5}$
3	$\frac{1}{1\cdot3}+\frac{1}{3\cdot5}+\frac{1}{5\cdot7}$	$\frac{15}{35}=\frac{3}{7}$
4	$\frac{1}{3}+\frac{1}{15}+\frac{1}{35}+\frac{1}{63}$	$\frac{28}{63}=\frac{4}{9}$
5	$\frac{1}{3}+\frac{1}{15}+\frac{1}{35}+\frac{1}{63}+\frac{1}{99}$	$\frac{45}{99}=\frac{5}{11}$
. . .		
6		$\frac{6}{13}$
7		$\frac{7}{15}$
. . .		
n		$\frac{n}{2n+1}$
. . .		
128	$\frac{1}{1\cdot3}+\ldots+\frac{1}{(2(128)-1)(2(128)+1)}$	$\frac{128}{2(128)+1}+\frac{128}{257}$

Page 43

M 5 km

Tu $\frac{a}{b}+\frac{c}{d}=\frac{a+c}{b+d} \rightarrow b^2c=-ad^2$

Some possibilities are:
(i) $a=c=0$,
(ii) $a=-c$ and $b=d$
(iii) $b^2=36$; $c=1$; $a=-4$; $d^2=9$
      $b=6$; $c=1$; $a=-4$; $d=3$
Are there other answers such as (iii)?

W 1

Th $1<\frac{d}{c}\le\frac{b}{a}\le\frac{bd}{ac}$

F 25%

$\frac{a}{a+w+1}=\frac{20}{100} \rightarrow 80a-20w=20$, and

$\frac{a+1}{a+w+1+1}=\frac{1}{3} \rightarrow 2a-w=-1$

So, $a=1$, $w=3$

Thus, $\frac{a}{a+w}=\frac{1}{1+3}=\frac{1}{4}=25\%$

Page 44

Patterns in Harmonic Triangle.
i.   1, ½, ⅓, ¼, ⅕, . . . down both sides
ii. 2nd diagonal is product of numbers from 1st; i.e.,
$$\tfrac{1}{1}\cdot\tfrac{1}{2}=\tfrac{1}{2}$$
$$\tfrac{1}{2}\cdot\tfrac{1}{3}=\tfrac{1}{6}$$
$$\tfrac{1}{3}\cdot\tfrac{1}{4}=\tfrac{1}{12}$$
iii. Symmetric about center line
iv. Denominators are multiples of Pascal's triangle:

1	x1: ⅟₁
1 1	x2: ½ ½
1 2 1	x3: ⅓ ⅙ ⅓
1 3 3 1	x4: ¼ ⅟₁₂ ⅟₁₂ ¼
1 4 6 4 1	x5: ⅕ ⅟₂₀ ⅟₃₀ ⅟₂₀ ⅕
1 5 10 10 5 1	x6: ⅙ ⅟₃₀ ⅟₆₀ ⅟₆₀ ⅟₃₀ ⅙

The 7th row is
⅟₇ ⅟₄₂ ⅟₁₀₅ ⅟₁₄₀ ⅟₁₀₅ ⅟₄₂ ⅟₇
The 8th row is
⅛ ⅟₅₆ ⅟₁₆₈ ⅟₂₈₀ ⅟₂₈₀ ⅟₁₆₈ ⅟₅₆ ⅛

½ + ⅙ + ⅟₁₂ + ⅟₂₀ + ⅟₃₀ + . . .
= 1 − ½ + ½ − ⅓ + ⅓ − ¼ + ¼ −
⅕ + ⅕ − ⅙ + . . . = 1, since all others add to 0.

Page 45

M $x+1$

Tu Bone setter

W $a(x-1)(x-2)(x-3)(x-4)(x-5)$ where a can be any nonzero constant

Th None:
$\frac{a}{b}+\frac{b}{a}=n \rightarrow a^2+b^2=nab \rightarrow$
$(a^2-nab+b^2)=0 \rightarrow (a-b)(a-b)$
so $n=2 \rightarrow a=b$

F x^2-3

Page 46

Some perfect numbers are:
   6 ($n=2$ in Euclid's formula)
  28 ($n=3$ in Euclid's formula)
 496 ($n=5$ in Euclid's formula)
8128 ($n=7$ in Euclid's formula)

Some amicable pairs are: 17,296 and 18,416; 1184 and 1210.

It is suggested that students write a computer program to determine amicable pairs of numbers up to some reasonable limit.

Page 47

M	$2\sqrt{5}$ and $3\sqrt{3}$
Tu	False. 2^{216091} is not prime since it is divisible by 2. (In 1985, $2^{216091} - 1$ was discovered to be the largest prime known to date.)
W	$x = 5$
Th	$10^9 = (2\cdot5)^9 = 2^9 \cdot 5^9$
F	500 km

Page 48

n	2	3	4	5	6	7	8	9	10	11	12	13	14
$d(n)$	2	2	3	2	4	2	4	3	4	2	6	2	4

n	15	16	17	19	25	27	30	36	41	49	53	64
$d(n)$	4	5	2	2	3	4	8	9	2	3	2	7

1. 2
2. 3
3. 4
4. $n + 1$
5. a square of an integer

Page 49

M	nth term can be $(-1)^{n+1}$ or $(-1)^{n-1}$. There are any number of equivalent expressions.
Tu	addition (+)
W	No. $3(2) > 2(1) + 1$
Th	

F	$x^3 - 7x + 6 = (x+3)(x-2)(x-1)$

Page 50

Team Score	Points Used
1	not possible
2	not possible
3	3
4	not possible
5	not possible
6	3 + 3
7	7
8	not possible
9	3 + 3 + 3
10	3 + 7
11	not possible
12	3 + 3 + 3 + 3
13	3 + 7 + 3
14	7 + 7
15	3 + 3 + 3 + 3 + 3

Using 3 and 7, 11 will be the largest number that cannot be obtained.

Using 4 and 7, the table looks like

Score	Points Used
1	not possible
2	not possible
3	not possible
4	4
5	not possible
6	not possible
7	7
8	4 + 4
9	not possible
10	not possible
11	7 + 4
12	4 + 4 + 4
13	not possible
14	7 + 7
15	7 + 4 + 4
16	4 + 4 + 4 + 4
17	not possible
18	7 + 7 + 4
19	4 + 4 + 4 + 7
20	4 + 4 + 4 + 4 + 4
21	7 + 7 + 7
22	7 + 7 + 4 + 4

All the other numbers are obtainable: add a multiple of 4 to the appropriate expression for 18, 19, 20, or 21.

Using 3 and 8, the largest unobtainable score is 13. Students should construct a table.

Using 5 and 7, the largest unobtainable score is 23. For 5 and 8, it is 27. For 4 and 9, it is 23. For 3 and 6, there is no largest unobtainable number. There is none for 4 and 8 either.

Notice that if one score is a multiple of the other score, then you get only team scores that are multiples of the lower score. In the case of 3 and 6, we could never get a 50, a 7000, or any number not divisible by 3.

For the other numbers, like 3 and 7, 4 and 7, etc., we are looking at numbers that are relatively prime. If the two scores a and b are relatively prime, then the largest number that cannot be obtained is $ab - (a+b)$. It is a good exercise to ask students to guess this generalization.

Page 51

M -2

Tu $(a+b)^2 = a^2 + 2ab + b2$

W

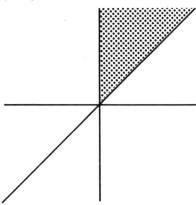

Th $5\frac{5}{11}$ minutes past 1:00

F $a(x+2)(x-3) = 0,\ a \rightarrow 0$
or $a(x^2 - x - 6) = 0,\ a \neq 0$

Page 52

Q1. During the time from 12:00 noon to 1:00 p.m., the minute hand moves 12 times as fast as the hour hand. Thus, the minute hand covers $\frac{12}{13}$ of an hour while the hour hand covers $\frac{1}{13}$. Thus, Lori spent $55\frac{5}{13}$ minutes on lunch.

Let x denote the number of minutes past noon at which Lori goes to lunch; during this same time, the hour hand moves $(\frac{1}{12})x$ minutes past 12. Thus, as she leaves for lunch, the hands are $(\frac{11}{12})x$ minutes apart. Since this distance is $\frac{1}{13}$ of 60 minutes, we must have

$(\frac{11}{12})x = \frac{1}{13} \cdot 60$; or $x = 5\frac{5}{143}$ min.

Thus, Lori left for lunch at 12:05$\frac{5}{143}$ p.m., stayed out for lunch for $55\frac{5}{13}$ minutes, and returned for work at 1:00$\frac{60}{143}$ p.m.

Q2. At 4:00, the hour hand is at 20 minutes. The minute hand moves $(\frac{1}{12})y$ minutes from 20 each time the minute hand moves y minutes. In order for the minute hand to pass the hour hand by 30 minutes, we must have

$20 + \frac{1}{12}y + 30 = y$.

This simplifies to $y = 54\frac{6}{11}$ minutes.

Thus, Craig finishes his problem at 4:54$\frac{6}{11}$ p.m., the total time he spent on the problem was $32\frac{8}{11}$ minutes because minute and hour hands are together at 4:21$\frac{9}{11}$.

Page 53

M   (13, 156), (14, 84), (15, 60), (16, 48), (18, 36), (20, 30), (21, 28), (24, 24), (28, 21), (30, 20), (36, 18), (48, 16), (60, 15), (84, 14) (156, 13)

Tu   Abacus

W   18 and 2

Th   4. Powers of 2 form a pattern 2, 4, 8, 6, 2, 4, 8, 6, ... beginning at $n = 1$. Thus, 2^{74} will have 4 as the units digit.

F   4

Page 54

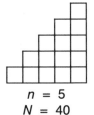

$n = 5$
$N = 40$

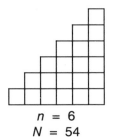

$n = 6$
$N = 54$

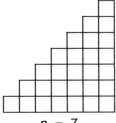

$n = 7$
$N = 70$

The following pattern develops:

n	N
1	4
2	10
3	18
4	28
5	40
6	54
7	70

A formulation is $N_n + N_{n-1} + 2(n+1)$ where $N_0 = 0$. The student is only expected to find N for $n = 5, 6, 7$. Students may be challenged to come up with this general formulation.

Some students may even note that $N(n) = n(n+3)$ produces a general formula for N.

Page 55

M $x^2 = 7$

Tu -1

W

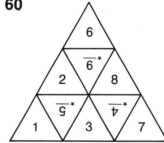

Th A

F $\dfrac{x\,(\sqrt{7} + \sqrt{3})}{4}$

Page 56

30	39	48	1	10	19	28
38	47	7	9	18	27	29
46	6	8	17	26	35	37
5	14	16	25	34	36	45
13	15	24	33	42	44	4
21	23	32	41	43	3	12
22	31	40	49	2	11	20

Page 57

M   B

Tu the Pythagoreans

W   Zero. $x^4 + x^2 + 1 > 0$ for all x.

Th $x^2 - y^2 = (x+y)\,(x-y) = 48$
Integer products giving 48 are $1{\cdot}48$; $2{\cdot}24$; $3{\cdot}16$; $4{\cdot}12$; $6{\cdot}8$. Integral solutions are possible when $x+y = 12$ and $x-y = 4$; or $x+y = 8$ and $x-y = 6$. Thus, answers are $x = 8$, $y = 4$; $x = 7$, $y = 1$.

F   A. hyperbola; B. ellipse; C. parabola

Page 58

$$2^1 + 2^2 + 2^3 + \ldots + 2^n = 2^{n+1} - 2$$
$$2^0 + 2^1 + 2^2 + \ldots + 2^n = 2^{n+1} - 1$$

Page 59

M   Around 23 runs

Tu The discriminant

W $y = 6$

Th $\dfrac{1}{x} > \dfrac{1}{x+1}$, for $x > 0$ and $x < -1$

      $\dfrac{1}{x+1} > \dfrac{1}{x}$, for $-1 < x < 0$

      For $x = 0$ and $x = -1$, the terms cannot be compared.

F $a = 1$; $a = 5$

Page 60

*These triangles are literally turned upside down in order to match roots.

Page 61

M   A circle of radius 2 with center at the point (3, 6)

Tu Hypatia

W   Zero

Th True. Can you prove it?

F $(9r - 11s)^2$

Page 62

n	1	2	3	4	5	6	7	8	...
T(n)	1	3	6	10	15	21	28	36	

From the table we see that T(n) = T($n-1$) + n, if we define T($n-1$) = 0.

A general formula for T(n) = $\dfrac{n(n+1)}{2}$, $n \geq 1$

n	1	2	3	4	5	6	7	8	...
S(n)	1	4	9	16	25	36	49	64	

From the table, we note that S(n) = S($n-1$) + ($2n-1$). It is also true that S(n) = n^2.

Page 63

M   2

Tu   Reverse alphabetical order

W $b = +13$; $b = -13$

Th $(a+b+c)^2 = a^2 + b^2 + c^2 + 2ab + 2ac + 2bc$

Notice:

a^2

b^2

c^2

ab

bc

ac

F $\dfrac{x-1}{x+1}$

Page 64

The triangular numbers are
1, 3, 6, 10, 15, 21, . . .
Thus, the first generalization could be

$$n^3 = \left(\frac{n(n+1)}{2}\right)^2 - \left(\frac{(n-1)n}{2}\right)^3$$

because $\dfrac{n(n+1)}{2} = \displaystyle\sum_{i=1}^{n} i.$

The second generalization could be derived from

$1^3 + 2^3 = 3^2 - 1^2 + 1^2 - 0^2$

$1^3 + 2^3 + 3^3 = 6^2 - 3^2 + 3^2 - 1^2 + 1^2 - 0^2$

$1^3 + 2^3 + 3^3 + 4^3 = 10^2 - 6^2 + 6^2 - 3^2 + 3^2 - 1^2 + 1^2 - 0^2$

or

$1^3 + 2^3 + 3^3 + 4^3 = 10^2 = \left(\dfrac{4(5)}{2}\right)^2$

$1^3 + 2^3 + 3^3 + \ldots + n^3 = \left(\dfrac{n(n+1)}{2}\right)^2$

Students should check these with several numbers.

Page 65

M $(x-6)^2 + (y-6)^2 = 36$

Tu   Computer

W   (3, 0)

Th   A quadrilateral with two right angles

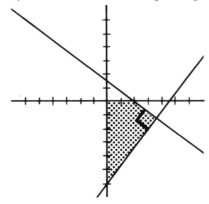

F $a = 100$; 117; 126; 145; 155; 176; or 187

82

Page 66

Represent each color by its first letter, then the relationships expressed as equations become

(i) $Y + B = G + M$

(ii) $P = R + V + S$

(iii) $B + O + P + V = M + G + T + S + W + Y$

(iv) $G = T + P + Y$

Each of these letters is the cube of a whole number from 1 to 12.

Trial and error indicates that equation (i) has only one solution: $1^3 + 12^3 = 9^3 + 10^3$.

Reviewing the second equation, and doing considerable arithmetic, we see solutions such as:

$12^3 = 6^3 + 8^3 + 10^3$

$9^3 = 1^3 + 6^3 + 8^3$

$6^3 = 3^3 + 4^3 + 5^3$

Since 1, 12, 9, and 10 must be used to satisfy equation (i), equation (ii) must be $6^3 = 3^3 + 4^3 + 5^3$. So, $P = 6^3$.

Several applications of trial and error with the values of (i) and (ii) and equation (iii) produce the following:

$Y = 1^3$; $V = 3^3$; $S = 4^3$; $O = 7^3$; $B = 12^3$; $T + W = 2^3 + 8^3$; and $M + G = 10^3 + 9^3$. Using equation (iv), and your calculator, you arrive at: $W = 2^3$; $T = 8^3$; $G = 9^3$; and $M = 10^3$.

Using values for P, V, and S and equation (ii), we conclude $R = 5^3$. Thus, $C = 11^3$, the only remaining number. Thus, color to number size corresponding is: Yellow-1, White-2, Violet-3, Silver-4, Red-5, Purple-6, Orange-7, Tangerine-8, Green-9, Mauve-10, Crimson-11, Blue-12.

Page 67

M If x and y are integers, then $3x + 6y$ will always be a multiple of 3. 92 is not a multiple of 3.

Tu Yes; Yes

W None. $x^2 + y^2 = 100$ is a circle of radius 10 and $x^2 + 2y^2 = 8$ is an ellipse with major axis of length $2 + \sqrt{2}$. Both figures are centered at the origin.

Th $ax + y = a^2 \equiv y = -ax + a^2$

$x + ay = 1 \equiv y = -\frac{1}{a} \cdot x + \frac{1}{a}$, $a \neq 0$.

If $a = \frac{1}{a}$ or $a^2 = 1$ (i.e., $a = \pm 1$) then lines have same slope.

If $a = +1$, $a^2 = 1$, $\frac{1}{a} = 1$, so lines are the same. $\therefore$ infinitely many solutions. If $a = -1$, $a^2 = 1$, $\frac{1}{a} = -1$ so lines are parallel; no solutions.

If $a \neq 0, 1, -1$, then lines intersect; one solution.

If $a = 0$, $y = 0$ and $x = 1$; one solution.

F 27

Page 68

There are many patterns:

1. Triangular numbers increase by 2, 3, 4, 5, etc.
2. Square numbers increase by 3, 5, 7, 9, 11, etc.
3. Pentagonal numbers increase by 4, 7, 10, 13, 16, etc.
4. Hexagonal numbers increase by 5, 9, 13, 17, 21, 25, etc.

Note: Each *increase* is an arithmetic sequence.

5. Several column patterns (increases): 1st by 0; 2nd by 1; 3rd by 3; 4th by 6; 5th by 10; nth by the $(n-1)$ triangular number.
6. Thus, each row is the sum of the row entry directly above and the triangular number in the column right before: i.e.,

$S_n = T_n + T_{n-1}$

$P_n = S_n + T_{n-1}$

$H_x n = P_n + T_{n-1}$

$H_n = H_x n + T_{n-1}$

$O_n = H_n + T_{n-1}$

This final pattern is used in a later poster puzzle. The tenth number in each row is as follows: Triangular-55; Square-100; Pentagonal-145; Hexagonal-190; Heptagonal-235; Octagonal-280.

Page 69

M Intersection is empty.

Tu Pebble. Merchants used to set out pebbles in grooves of sand to calculate and add up accounts.

W -3

Th False. For example, $-\sqrt{5} + \sqrt{5} = 0$.

F 2:1

Page 70

One dice has sides 0, 0, 0, 6, 6, 6.
The other has sides 1, 2, 3, 4, 5, 6.
The 36 ordered pairs possible are:

(0, 1) (0, 1) (0, 1) (6, 1) (6, 1) (6, 1)
(0, 2) (0, 2) (0, 2) (6, 2) (6, 2) (6, 2)
(0, 3) (0, 3) (0, 3) (6, 3) (6, 3) (6, 3)
(0, 4) (0, 4) (0, 4) (6, 4) (6, 4) (6, 4)
(0, 5) (0, 5) (0, 5) (6, 5) (6, 5) (6, 5)
(0, 6) (0, 6) (0, 6) (6, 6) (6, 6) (6, 6)

Each sum 1, 2, 3, . . . , 12 occurs 3 of 36 times.

Page 71

M K = 2

Tu

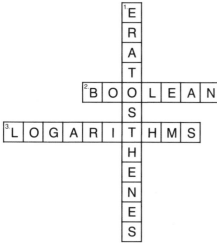

W $a > 0$; $a = 0$; $a < 0$

Th 14.5

F $2\sqrt{12}$ or $4\sqrt{3}$

Page 72

Show: $P(n) = S(n) + T(n-1)$.
$S(n) + T(n-1)$

$$= n^2 + \frac{(n-1)^2 + (n-1)}{2}$$

$$= \frac{2n^2 + n^2 - 2n + 1 + n - 1}{2}$$

$$= \frac{3n^2 - n}{2} = P(n)$$

Show: $Hx(n) = P(n) + T(n-1)$.
$P(n) + T(n-1)$

$$= \frac{3n^2 - n}{2} + \frac{(n-1)^2 + (n-1)}{2}$$

$$= \frac{3n^2 - n + n^2 - 2n + 1 + n - 1}{2}$$

$$= \frac{4n^2 - 2n}{2} = 2n^2 - n = Hx(n)$$

Show: $H(n) = Hx(n) + T(n-1)$
$Hx(n) + T(n-1)$

$$= 2n^2 - n + \frac{(n-1)^2 + (n-1)}{2}$$

$$= \frac{4n^2 - 2n + n^2 - 2n + 1 + n - 1}{2}$$

$$= \frac{5n^2 - 3n}{2} = H(n)$$

According to pattern:
$O(n) = H(n) + T(n-1)$

$$= \frac{5n^2 - 3n}{2} + \frac{(n-1)^2 + (n-1)}{2}$$

$$= \frac{5n^2 - 3n + n^2 - 2n + 1 + n - 1}{2}$$

$$= \frac{6n^2 - 4n}{2} = 3n^2 - 2n$$

Again, using pattern,
$N(n) = O(n) + T(n-1)$

$$= 3n^2 - 2n + \frac{(n-1)^2 + (n-1)}{2}$$

$$= \frac{6n^2 - 4n + n^2 - 2n + 1 + n - 1}{2}$$

$$= \frac{7n^2 - 5n}{2}.$$

NOTES